DAVID COPPERFIELD

in Copperplate

Forty-six illustrations
for the famous Dickens novel augmented by interpretative short passages
taken from the original text

BY WILLIAM ROSS CAMERON

PUBLISHED BY BERN PORTER · BERKELEY, CALIFORNIA

1947

PUBLISHER'S NOTE

In offering this series of drawings by William Ross Cameron, the publisher is confident that their charm will be apparent to collectors & amateurs alike. Collectors of Dickensiana will find in them a fresh interpretation of David Copperfield, so often essayed by other artists, so seldom successfully. Through his painstaking researches into the life and manners of the period and through his piquant characterization—often just this side of caricature—that is *Dickens, Will Cameron has added another bouquet to the great Victorian's wreath. Whether or not they have ever read the 800-odd pages of the novel amateurs from "seven to seventy" will find in these plates, with accompanying excerpts from the original text, a personally conducted tour of vivacity and sustained interest through the stirring scenes of David's fortunes & misfortunes. Children of seven will be led to read this truly remarkable novel, and those of seventy to reread and relive it!*

My aunt said never a word, but took her bonnet by the strings, in the manner of a sling . . . aimed a blow at Mr Chillip's head with it, put it on bent, walked out, and never came back.

"Confusion to Brooks of Sheffield!" The toast was received with great applause, and such hearty laughter that it made me laugh too . . . at which they laughed the more. In short, we quite enjoyed ourselves.

"Yon's our house, Mas'r Davy!" There was a black barge, or some other kind of superannuated boat, not far off, high and dry on the ground, with an iron funnel sticking out of it for a chimney and smoking very cosily; but nothing else in the way of a habitation that was visible to me.

We were the admiration of Mrs Gummidge and Peg-gotty, who used to whisper of an evening when we sat lovingly, on our little locker side by side,"Lor! wasn't it beautiful!" Mr Peggotty smiled at us from behind his pipe, & Ham grinned all the evening & did nothing else.

But the greatest effect of these miserable lessons is when my mother (thinking nobody is observing her), tries to give me the cue by the motion of her lips. At that instant Miss Murdstone, who has been lying in wait for nothing else all along, says in a deep warning voice: "Clara!"

Accordingly we looked in at a baker's window, and after I had made a series of proposals to buy everything that was bilious in the shop, & he had rejected them one by one, we decided in favour of a nice little loaf of brown bread . . . which cost me threepence.

I begged him to do me the favour of presiding. . . .
As to me, I sat on his left hand, and the rest were
grouped about us, on the nearest beds & on the floor.

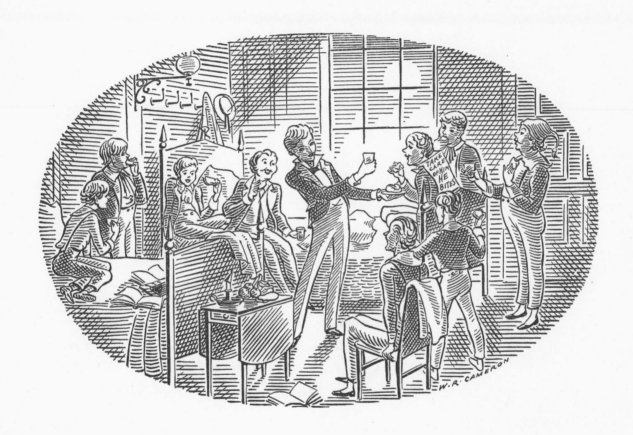

Prsently the tune left off, & a good-looking young fellow came across the yard into the room. He had a hammer in his hand, & his mouth was full of little nails, which he was obliged to take out before he could speak. "Well, Joram!" said Mr Omer. "How do you get on?"

"This," said the stranger, with a certain condescending roll in his voice, & a certain indescribable air of doing something genteel, which impressed me very much, *"is Master Copperfield. I hope I see you well, sir?"*

I have known him to come home to supper with a flood of tears, and a declaration that nothing was now left but a jail; & go to bed making a calculation of the expense of putting bow-windows to the house, "in case anything turned up," which was his favourite expression.

*The woman burst into a fit of laughter, as
if she thought this a joke, & tossed it back
to me, nodded once, as slightly as before,
and made the word "Go!" with her lips.*

W. R. CAMERON

"If you please, aunt, I am your nephew." "Oh, Lord!"
said my aunt. And sat down flat in the garden path.

"You can go when you like . . . I'll take my chance with the boy. If he's all you say he is, at least I can do as much for him then, as you have done. But I don't believe a word of it!"

When the pony-chaise stopped at the door, & my eyes were intent upon the house, I saw a cadaverous face appear at a small window on the ground floor (in a little round tower that formed one side of the house), and quickly disappear.

"I suppose you are quite a great lawyer?" I said, after looking at him for some time. . . . "Me, Master Copper- field?" said Uriah. "Oh, no! I'm a very umble person."

"Copperfield! Is it possible?" It was Mr Micawber, with his eye-glass, and his walking-stick, and his shirt-collar, and his genteel air, & the condescending roll in his voice, all complete!

I grasped him by both hands and could not let them go. But for very shame, and the fear that I might displease him, I could have held him round the neck and cried.

"He was very generous and noble to me in those days, I assure you, ma'am," said I . . . "and I stood in need of such a friend. I should have been quite crushed without him." "He is always generous and noble," said Mrs Steerforth, proudly.

"That is a black shadow to be following the girl,"
said Steerforth, standing still; "what does it mean?

"You're a pretty fellow!" said Miss Mowcher, after a brief inspection. "You'd be as bald as a friar on the top of your head in twelve months, but for me."

... *my attention was distracted by observing that the handy young man went out of the room very often, and that his shadow always presented itself, immediately afterwards, on the wall of the entry, with a bottle at its mouth. The "young gal" likewise occasioned me some uneasiness: not so much by neglecting to wash the plates, as by breaking them.*

There I saw him, lying on his back, with his legs extending to I don't know where, gurglings taking place in his throat, stoppages in his nose, and his mouth open like a post-office.

All was over in a moment. I had fulfilled my destiny. I was a captive and a slave . . . I loved Dora Spenlow to distraction!

"My dear," said Mr Micawber, leading her towards me, "here is a gentleman of the name of Copperfield, who wishes to renew his acquaintance with you."

And she had struck him, & had thrown him off with the fury of a wild cat, and had burst out of the room.

I was on the point of asking him if he knew me, when he tried to stretch out his arm, and said to me, distinctly, with a pleasant smile: "Barkis is willin'!"

The face he turned up to the troubled sky, the quivering of his clasped hands, the agony of his figure, remain associated with that lonely waste, in my remembrance, to this hour.

" 'Unless he brings me back a lady," said Mr Peggotty, tracing out that part with his finger. "I come
to know, ma'am, whether he will keep his wured?"

I don't know how I did it. I did it in a moment. I intercepted Jip. I had Dora in my arms. I was full of eloquence . . . I never stopped for a word.

I shall never forget him peeping round the corner of the street in Tottenham Court Road, while Peggotty was bargaining for the precious articles . . .

"Deuce take the man!" said my aunt, sternly,
"what's he about? Don't be galvanic, sir!"

"My dear Copperfield," said Mr Micawber, rising with one of his thumbs in each of his waistcoat pockets, "…allow me, on the part of Mrs Micawber, myself, and our offspring, to thank them in the warmest & most uncompromising terms for their good wishes."

"No, thank you!" said Mr Spenlow, coldly, as I mechanically offered them back to him. "I will not deprive you of them. Miss Murdstone, be so good as to proceed."

"I know, Trotwood! My darling child and you—I know! But look at him!" He pointed to Uriah, pale and glowering in a corner, evidently very much out of his calculations, & taken by surprise.

It was Martha at the door. I saw her haggard, listening face distinctly. My dread was lest he should turn his head, and see her too.

Ultimately I found myself backing Traddles into the fire-place, & bowing in great confusion to two dry little elderly ladies, dressed in black . . . and each looking wonderfully like a preparation in chip or tan of the late Mr Spenlow.

"You villain," said I, "what do you mean by entrapping me into your schemes? How dare you appeal to me just now, you false rascal, as if we had been in discussion together?"

Of the clergyman & clerk appearing; of a few boatmen and some other people strolling in; of an ancient mariner behind me, strongly flavouring the church with rum; of the service beginning in a deep voice, and our all being very attentive.

"Annie!" cried the Doctor. "Not at my feet, my dear." "Yes!" she said. "I beg & pray that no one will leave the room! Oh, my husband and father . . . break this long silence. Let us both know what it is that has come between us!"

I inclined my head, without knowing what she meant; and she said, 'Come here!" again; and returned, followed by the respectable Mr Lattimer, who, with undiminished respectability, made me a bow, & took up his position behind her.

"Will you trust me?" she asked, in a low voice of astonishment. "Full and free!" said Mr Peggotty.

The foot upon the stairs came nearer—nearer—passed her as she went down—rushed into the room!"Uncle!"

"The Devil take you!" said Uriah, writhing in a new way with pain. "I'll be even with you."

He lies down at my feet, stretches himself out as if to sleep, and with a plaintive cry, is dead. . . . That face, so full of pity, and of grief, that rain of tears, that awful mute appeal to me, that solemn hand upraised towards Heaven!

"Lord bless me, yes!" said Traddles—"by the Reverend Horace—to Sophy—down in Devonshire. Why, my dear boy, she's behind the window curtain! Look here!"

My aunt . . . with one clap of her hands . . . and one look through her spectacles, immediately went into hysterics, for the first and only time in all my knowledge of her.